MW00603396

You are invited...

Grace of Gratitude Journal

Published by

Applegate Valley Publishing

Grants Pass, Oregon

www.graceofgratitude.com

ISBN #978-0-982775950

Illustrations by Tara Thelen

www.tara-artwork.com

Design by Deborah Perdue of Illumination Graphics

www.illuminationgraphics.com

Printed in Canada

Our Invitation to You...

This Gratitude Journal is not only for the novice, but also for anyone who is already experienced with the spiritual practice of feeling gratitude in his or her life.

We have filled this journal with a mixture of Tara Thelen's inspiring artwork and a sprinkling of "gratitudes" from Deborah Perdue's years of writing about the things she appreciates the most in her own life. We then invite readers to record their own thoughts of thanksgiving in the spaces provided.

As those who have experienced the Grace of Gratitude already know, feeling gratitude is a gateway to more bliss, contentment, well-being and peace in life. Feeling appreciative, feeling grateful, and recognizing the blessings in our lives can be a direct line to more joy! Sometimes the simplest things in life can go unnoticed, and the practice of journaling your gratitude will help you recognize so many more of the blessings in your life.

Being grateful will most certainly transform your life in powerful ways! If you are a novice, you can use this journal to get you started. Forty days of repeated practice will become a habit. So, if you are new to the spiritual practice of gratitude, there are ample pages to get you started. Writing in five or ten gratitudes per day as you feel inspired is a good beginning. Date each page and do your best to continue for forty consecutive days. You should soon notice how your spirit is uplifted and the practice becomes a natural part of your daily life.

If you are already a gratitude aficionado, we invite you to enjoy this beautiful journal as you continue on your path.

ENJOY!

Deborah L Perdue

I am thankful for ME
exactly as I am!

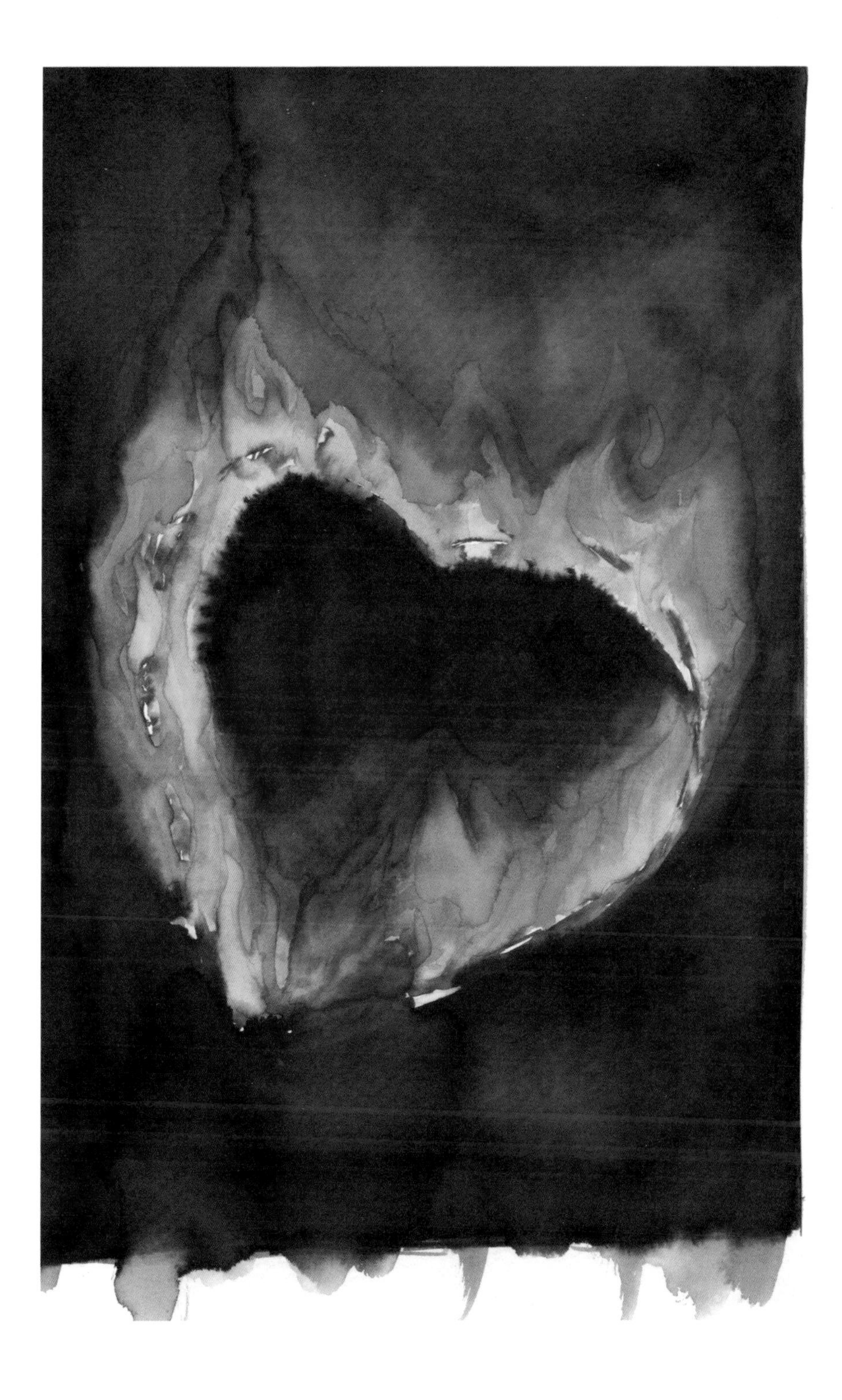

Date: ___________

I am grateful for:

I am so grateful
for the bounty
and splendor of nature
which nurtures me
each and every day.

Date: ____________

I am grateful for:

I am in gratitude
for limitless potential!

Date: ____________

I am grateful for:

Date: ____________

I am grateful for:

I am thankful
for my steadfast commitment
to peace, love, beauty & joy.

Date: ____________

I am grateful for:

Date: ______

I am grateful for:

I am deeply grateful
for my spiritual path
which keeps me growing,
changing, and realizing
the Divinity of life.

Date: ____________

I am grateful for:

Date: ____________

I am grateful for:

I am grateful
for my discernment
and good judgment –
I trust myself!

Date: ____________

I am grateful for:

I am grateful
for the amazing abundance
of all good that is streaming,
pouring, flowing into my life...

Date: ____________

I am grateful for:

Date: ____________

I am grateful for:

I am grateful
for my
joyful,
passionate heart.

Date: ____________

I am grateful for:

I am thankful
for my partner
and our cozy, comfortable,
harmonious life together.

Date: ____________

I am grateful for:

Date: __________

I am grateful for:

I am so grateful
for the magic
and unseen mysteries
of life.

Date: ______________

I am grateful for:

I am thankful
for the extravaganza
of Spring - the neon-green grass
on our meadow and the delightful
show of new birth and blossoms!

Date: ___________

I am grateful for:

Date: ____________

I am grateful for:

I am deeply grateful
for the shifting consciousness
of the earth's people.

Date: ____________

I am grateful for:

I am grateful
for the dazzling radiance
of the warm sunshine
today.

Date: __________

I am grateful for:

Date: __________

I am grateful for:

I am in deep gratitude
for the blessed pets
and animals
of this planet.

Date: ______________

I am grateful for:

I am thankful
for the deep knowing
that I am One with the One.

Date: ____________

I am grateful for:

Date: ___________

I am grateful for:

I am grateful for
the peace that permeates
my soul.

Date: ______________

I am grateful for:

I am thankful for my growing confidence, knowing that I am absolutely perfect exactly as I am!

Date: ____________

I am grateful for:

Date: ____________

I am grateful for:

Date: ____________

I am grateful for:

I am thankful
for every single expression of life;
tiny and vast,
stretching to infinity...

Date: __________

I am grateful for:

Thank you Spirit,
for each new day.

Date: ____________

I am grateful for:

Date: ____________

I am grateful for:

I am so very grateful
for my circle of friends, my tribe
of like-minded thinkers and the joy
they bring to my life.

Date: __________

I am grateful for:

*I am grateful for
a shining light-filled
snow-covered mountain
nearby...and the quiet
grace of falling snow.*

Date: ____________

I am grateful for:

Date: ____________

I am grateful for:

I am in gratitude
for love like a river,
flowing into my life…

Date: ____________

I am grateful for:

I am so grateful
for letting go
and letting things flow.

Date: ____________

I am grateful for:

Date: ____________

I am grateful for:

Thank you, Spirit,
for the universal language
and intrinsic beauty
of music and art!

Date: ____________

I am grateful for:

I am so grateful for time
opening up, more expansive
than I imagined...
providing spaciousness
and balance and grace
in my life

Date: ____________

I am grateful for:

I am in gratitude
for love and joy and peace
and grace and ease and truth and
beauty and wisdom...

Date: ___________

I am grateful for:

Date: ______________

I am grateful for:

All is well
and I am grateful.

Date: ____________

I am grateful for:

Thank you, Spirit within
and all around,
for all the knowledge
and wisdom
infusing my mind and soul.

Date: ____________

I am grateful for:

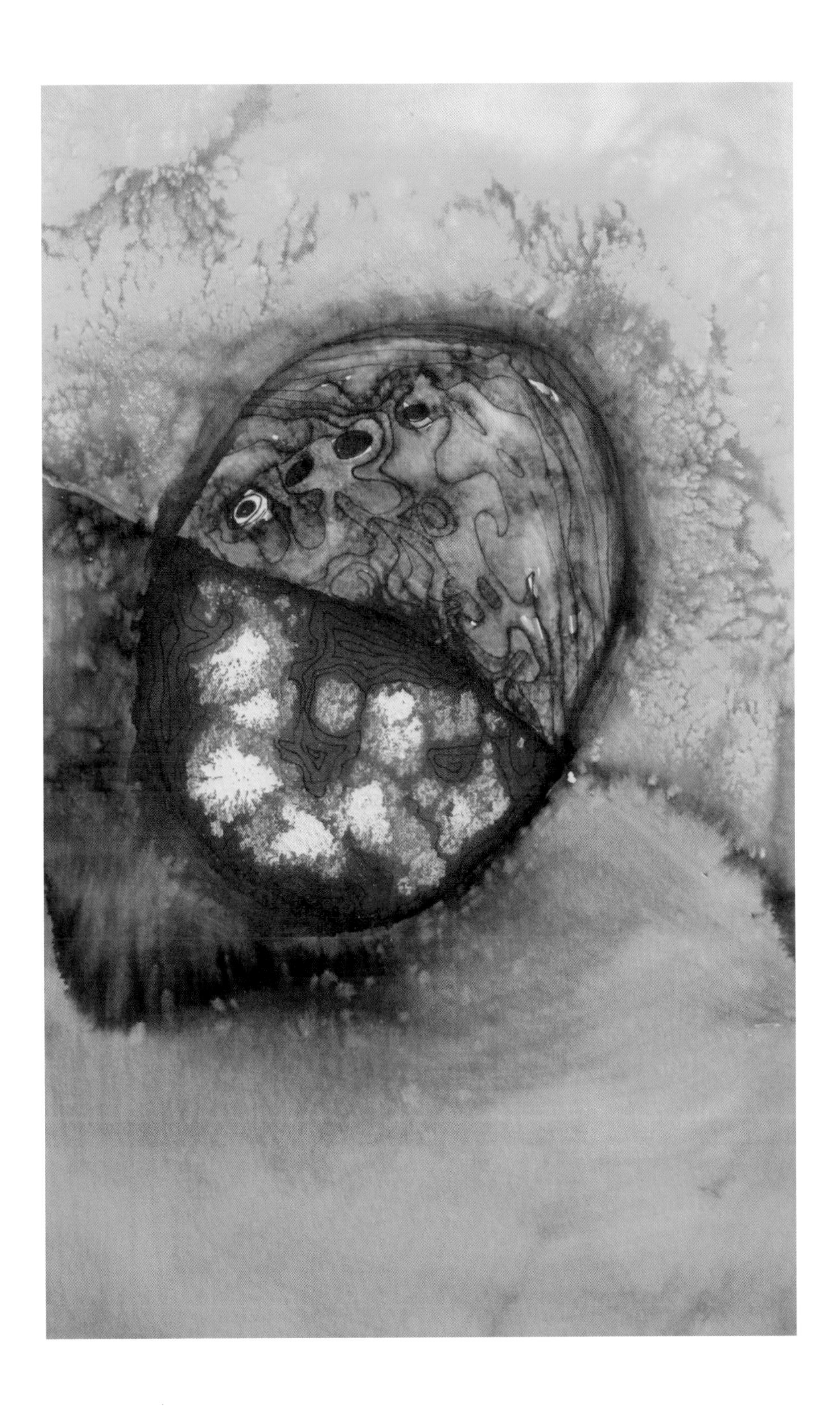

Date: ____________

I am grateful for:

I am grateful
for today,
with no plans
and no agenda!

Date: ____________

I am grateful for:

Thank you, Life,
for each new day!

Date: ____________

I am grateful for:

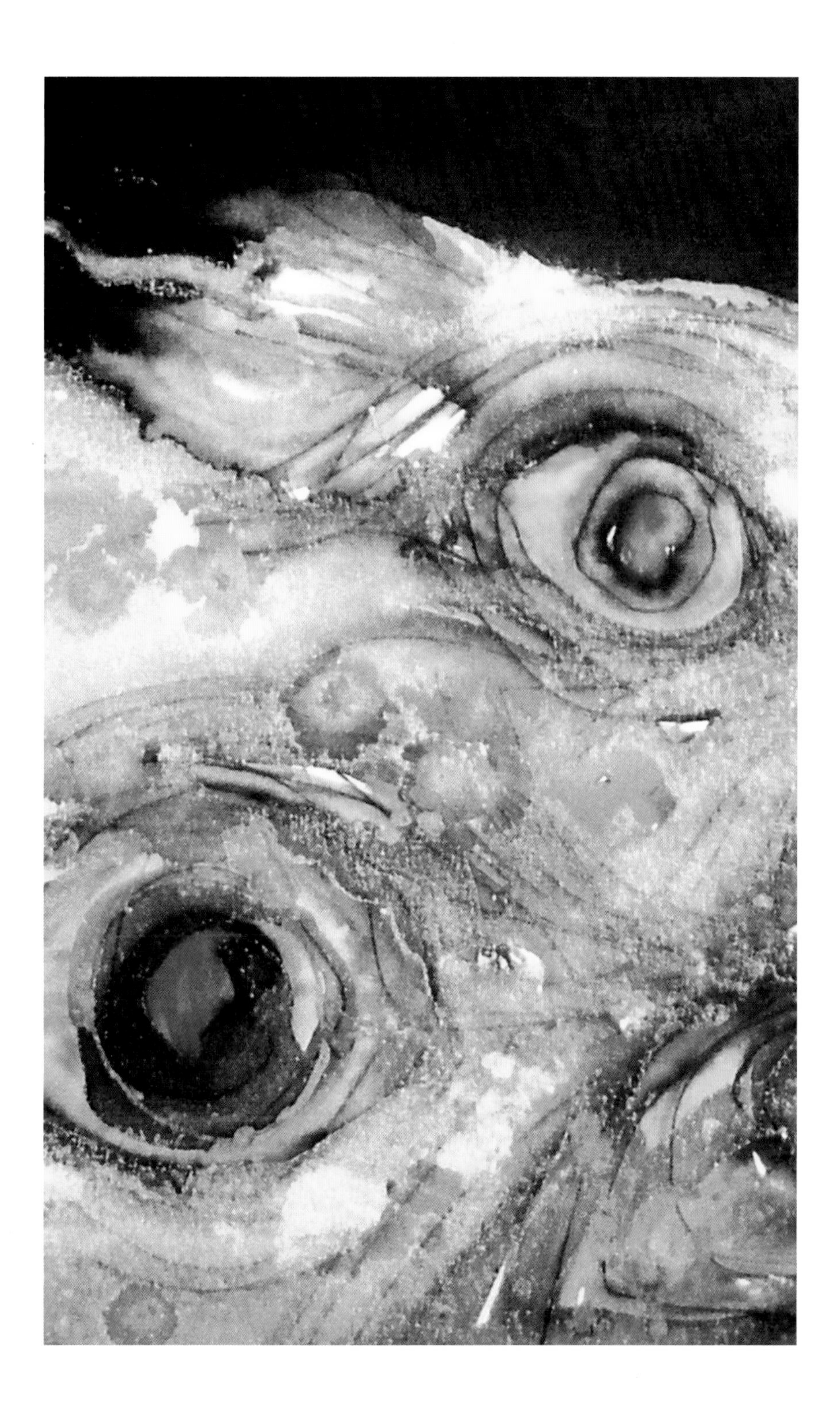

Date: ___________

I am grateful for:

I am so thankful
for my resolve, energy,
motivation,
and can-do attitude.

Date: ____________

I am grateful for:

Date: ____________

I am grateful for:

I am in gratitude
for the dazzling
golden light of Autumn
and the colorful
leaves falling like confetti
from the shedding trees.

Date: ____________

I am grateful for:

Date: ____________

I am grateful for:

Date: __________

I am grateful for:

Date: ______________

I am grateful for:

Date: ____________

I am grateful for:

About the Author & Illustrator

Deborah Perdue, RScP has been a licensed practitioner for the Centers for Spiritual Living since 2006. She lives in beautiful Southern Oregon on five acres with her husband and pups. Deborah teaches spiritual classes, and facilitates workshops and retreats on the topics of gratitude, abundance and how to live a life of joy. She has a chapter in the two books "The Energy of Expansion," and "The Energy of Creativity." She publishes blogs and articles on inner peace and gratitude. It is her intention to continue to expand the potent spiritual practice of gratitude in the world!

Tara Thelen is an American artist living near Amsterdam. The inspiration for her work is emotion in all its various forms. As an artist, Tara's drive is to create art that elicits strong, positive emotions – art that leaves an impression and truly touches those who view it. She teaches art lessons to children and teens at Museum Kranenburgh in the beautiful village of Bergen, near the North Sea, where she lives with her husband Paul and their two teenage boys. Her artwork has been exhibited in galleries throughout the US, Europe, and the Pacific.

Together we would like to say that we are grateful for having met each other through a "chance" email inquiry almost 10 years ago, which lead to an immediate collaboration – one that has developed professionally and personally over the years, through countless book design projects and various commercial endeavors, and to finally meeting in person for our Grace of Gratitude book signings in 2013 – and it's a collaboration that continues to grow and expand on every level!

Our gratitude goes to...

Susan and Chris van der Veen who believed in us, and helped and encouraged us to get the first printing of this Journal published.

And thank you with all of our hearts to our precious families & friends, and to the ones who have let us know that they have already been touched by the Grace of Gratitude Journal.

GO TO

www.graceofgratitude.com

for blogs, to sign up for Daily Gratitude Affirmations and to order more products including beautiful greeting cards.

Grace of Gratitude Journal Volume 2 to be published in 2015!

If you enjoy your Grace of Gratitude Journal, please take a moment to let other people know by posting a review on amazon.com. Thank you.

If you would like to be on our email list to hear of new products and other news, or simply to communicate with us, please email

info@graceofgratitude.com